House Sparrows

House Sparrows
Ragamuffins of the City

by J. J. McCoy

Drawings by Jean Zallinger

THE SEABURY PRESS · *New York*

To Robert G. Hudson
Fellow Naturalist and Friend

ACKNOWLEDGMENTS

The research and writing of a nonfiction book often require the help of others. I extend my gratitude to all those persons who have contributed to this book on the lore of the house sparrows.

I am especially grateful to Mrs. Clarence Yardley, who lives in "Sparrow House" in Philadelphia, for her comments about the house and John Bardsley.

I also wish to thank Mrs. Arthur Guiterman for permission to quote the poem by her husband, Arthur Guiterman, which appears in Chapter Six.

J. J. McC.

Contents

House Sparrows

CHAPTER ONE

Sparrow Jack

Many citizens of Philadelphia, the City of Brotherly
Love, lacked a brotherly feeling in the spring of
1868. At least, they did not feel kindly toward the
inchworms that were infesting the city.

Each spring the inchworms appeared, but this
year there seemed to be more than usual. Armies of
them marched across pavements and streets, and
crawled up hundreds of tree trunks. The loopers, as
the inchworms were sometimes called, dotted the
foliage of trees and shrubs, chewing the leaves into
lacework. They dangled from twigs and branches by
almost invisible threads, then dropped, wriggling,
onto the necks of irate Philadelphians.

The inchworms were destructive members of the
moth family known as *Geometridae* (Geo-MET-ri-
dee), or earth measurers. Actually, the inchworms
were the larva form of a moth. They advanced by

looping themselves—that is, they drew up their bodies in the middle into an inverted U-shape, then stretched themselves out flat. Thus, by alternately looping and flattening themselves, the little worms inched along.

Nothing stopped them, for the caterpillars had no enemies. Only a starving bird would eat an inchworm. And since there was plenty of food in the spring when the caterpillars appeared, the birds left them alone.

Fruit and shade trees alike suffered great damage as the pesky caterpillars simply ate their way through the foliage. Many of the trees, deprived of their breathing apparatus, withered and died. Some of these trees had been standing when William Penn first landed in what had become Philadelphia.

Naturally, people were annoyed and upset. Citizens whose trees and shrubs had been damaged by the worms complained to the City Council, demanding that something be done about the caterpillars. These were the days before DDT and other potent insecticides, so about all the Council could do was hire men to pick the inchworms by hand off trees and shrubs. However, there were so many caterpillars spread over so vast a region that this proved an endless and hopeless task.

The members of the City Council hoped a plague would come and kill off the inchworms. Unfortunately, none appeared and the hungry inchworms went right on nibbling leaves and tickling the necks of Philadelphians.

One citizen who was especially concerned about the situation was a house painter named John Bardsley. Bardsley lived in an old stone house in the historic Germantown section of Philadelphia, and his garden contained some fine trees and shrubs. Both house and garden had been used as observation points during the Revolutionary War Battle of Germantown in 1779.

Bardsley's trees did not escape the inchworms. The pests invaded his maple, oak, and beech trees, leaving only the evergreens alone. Bardsley valued his trees and constantly sought ways to get rid of the inchworms.

Many birds visited his garden. Robins, wrens, blue jays, woodpeckers, and thrushes were among the bird guests. While not a naturalist or ornithologist, Bardsley often watched these familiar birds catch and eat various insects. The robins and thrushes captured many worms, but not once did Bardsley ever see them, or any other birds, eat an inchworm. The loopers roamed unmolested.

One spring day, Bardsley was strolling through his garden. The inchworms were at work and he stared at one as it looped along a twig just a few feet in front of him. Surely, he thought, there must be some bird that ate the little green caterpillars. Then his thoughts drifted back to his native village of Ashton, England. He remembered some small birds that were abundant in the village and on nearby farms. These birds caught and ate many insects, including caterpillars. The stocky little birds were called house sparrows.

Memories of Ashton stirred John Bardsley. For some time he had been thinking of a trip back home. Now the recollection of the house sparrows excited him. Why hadn't he thought of them before? The house sparrows readily devoured English caterpillars; wasn't it possible that they would also eat American inchworms? The more he thought about the sparrows, the more determined he was to test his idea. Why not go to England, obtain some house sparrows and bring them back to Philadelphia?

Bardsley decided to discuss his idea with William Smith, a member of the City Council. It was more than likely that he would welcome any idea that might help rid the city of caterpillars.

Councilman Smith and John Bardsley held a conference, and Smith listened attentively while Bardsley told how the sparrows helped Ashton gardeners and farmers by destroying countless caterpillars, as well as other harmful beetles and bugs. Then Bardsley brought up the idea of a trip to England to collect house sparrows for export to Philadelphia.

The Councilman mulled over Bardsley's proposal. The tale of the house sparrows had impressed him and he agreed that the project was worth a trial. Besides, nobody had come forward with a better one. About how many sparrows did Bardsley expect to bring back? Bardsley's answer came quickly: one thousand birds.

Smith put forth some more questions. If the sparrows were so valuable, would England permit them to be exported in such a large number? How much would it cost to obtain and ship the birds? And, most important, would the house sparrows survive in Philadelphia? Councilman Smith reminded Bardsley of the sparrows imported into New York and Boston some years earlier. Those birds had failed to adapt to their new environment.

Bardsley admitted that he did not know the answers to all of Smith's questions. However, he did think that the sparrows—or at least some of them—would survive in Philadelphia. New York and Boston had imported only a few birds; he proposed to bring in many more and thus assure a better chance of survival. He pointed out, too, that the sparrows were very hardy birds. They were found throughout Europe, he had learned, and some of the countries in which they lived had climates very similar to that of Philadelphia.

The two men became more and more enthusiastic as they explored the possibilities of the house sparrows. By the end of their conversation Smith was completely won over by Bardsley's plan. However, he could not authorize a sparrow expedition on his own. Only the City Council had the power to approve such a project. He promised to bring the matter up at their next meeting.

Smith kept his word and outlined Bardsley's idea to the City Council. Eager to rid the city of inchworms, the members listened carefully. But they wanted more information about Bardsley's sparrow project: how much it would cost, whether England would allow the sparrows to leave the country, and the answers to other questions. Finally the Council voted to withhold its approval until Bardsley submitted the needed data. Meanwhile the inchworms went right on plundering the city's trees.

Naturally, Bardsley was disappointed by the City Council's failure to approve his plan. He realized that there were two ways of obtaining the information the Council required: write to friends in England or go there himself. He decided to seek the answers abroad, combining a visit to Ashton with the sparrow project.

Bardsley was ready to sail for England at the end of summer. He had hoped for some temporary approval from the City Council, but there was still no word. However, even though he was not a wealthy man, Bardsley was determined to continue with his plan. If it were successful it would be a boon to the entire community—and, of course, to his own garden too. He took leave of his family and friends and sailed for England.

Bardsley arrived in Ashton nearly a month later, and after visiting with his relatives he started work on his sparrow project. First, he checked into the matter of taking sparrows out of England. He already knew that the United States had no law against importing birds. The British authorities gladly gave their consent to the exportation of house sparrows; there were plenty for everybody. Next came the matter of finding enough boxes or pens to hold the thousand sparrows he expected to catch. These he was able to secure within a short time

Bardsley informed the Philadelphia City Council of his progress, then set about the task of trapping house sparrows. Almost every one of Ashton's young boys offered to help him gather the birds. The boys often went sparrow hunting and brought birds home for the family dinner. Although small, they made a tasty meal.

House sparrows were everywhere in Ashton, but

the young sparrow hunters warned Bardsley that the birds were not easy to catch. While they were tame, the sparrows were also wary. They cleverly avoided traps and snares, so it was foolish to set a trap and hope that the sparrows would hop into it.

The trick, according to the boys, was to use "sparrow poles." Bardsley examined one of them. It was simply a long pole with a large butterfly-like net attached to one end. However, the net or bag was considerably stronger than the type used for catching butterflies. A sparrow could easily break out of a butterfly net, the boys explained.

It was best to snare the sparrows after the birds had gone to roost for the night. Then the sparrow hunters could quietly lift the birds off their perches with the sparrow poles.

Bardsley and his youthful sparrow hunters stalked the birds at dusk. Each night they added more sparrows to the collection and housed them in boxes or pens. Thanks to the Ashton boys, Bardsley collected his one thousand sparrows in a shorter time than he had expected. Now all that remained to be done was to transfer the birds to shipping cages and convey them to the port of Liverpool.

Bardsley had purchased cages made of reeds which would be the homes of the sparrows while at sea. Several birds were put into one cage. When all of the cages were occupied, wagons carried the chirping birds to the seaport. As the tuneful caravan rolled toward Liverpool, many people stopped to eye and listen to the strange cargo. Some of them must have wondered what anyone could possibly want with all those sparrows.

In Liverpool, Bardsley concluded the final arrangements for shipping the sparrows and supervised the loading of the precious cargo. Since the birds would need food and water during the voyage, it was necessary to stow them where they could easily be reached. Also, the cages had to be secured against storms and rough seas. Bardsley checked every cage before the ship sailed. After all, he had spent a lot of time and money on the project, and he did not want to lose any of the valuable sparrows.

Just before the ship sailed from Liverpool, Bardsley

received some good news. The Philadelphia City Council had approved his project. Now he would not have to bear the expense of gathering and shipping the birds.

There were some uneasy moments on the crossing to Philadelphia. Storms raised rough waters and the ship tossed back and forth. Fortunately, the birds took the journey well, and as far as Bardsley could tell, none of them were seasick. He saw to it that the sparrows were well fed; there was plenty of cracked grain on board ship. If the sparrows minded being cooped up in their reed cages, they gave no sign.

John Bardsley and his sparrows arrived in Philadelphia in March, 1869. No welcoming committee or delegation greeted them. A lone and curious reporter for the Philadelphia *Public Ledger and Daily Transcript* lounged on the dock. He watched as stevedores unloaded cage after cage of chirping sparrows. Then, when the last cage was stacked onto horse-drawn wagons, he wandered off to file his news item.

The landing of the sparrows produced mixed emotions. Many people scoffed at the idea: if no American bird would eat inchworms, no foreign bird would, either. Philadelphia naturalists and ornithologists also had doubts about the sparrows. Since the birds were not a native species, they pointed out, it was doubtful if they would eat unfamiliar insects. Other people were willing to wait and see what the sparrows would do.

March can be a cold and windy month in Philadelphia. Therefore, Bardsley and the City Council decided to keep the sparrows in boxes until the weather changed. Some of the sparrows were placed in Bardsley's own care. He erected weather-proof bird boxes on one wall of his house in Germantown and put a pair of sparrows in each one. Other interested persons were given sparrows to keep until the birds could safely be released in the city. It was very important to protect the sparrows during this first cold month, if they were to survive in their new country.

March gave way to April and signs of spring became stronger. Most of Bardsley's brigade of sparrows had survived. As soon as the weather turned warm enough, the birds were released in various parts of Philadelphia. Those areas that had been hardest hit by inchworms the previous year received priority.

The warm days of late May and early June brought out the annual parade of caterpillars, and the worms quickly spread through the trees. Everyone's eyes were on the sparrows. What would the birds do?

Despite the fact that they were on trial, the sparrows at first ignored the caterpillars and calmly went about the business of the season. They paired off, built nests, and started to rear nestlings.

The townspeople began to despair. They didn't know that baby sparrows require an enormous amount of food—and that they are fed exclusively on insects or the various forms of insects, like larvae, etc. Back and forth from the nests flew the sparrow parents. They swiftly snatched up the abundant inchworms and dropped them into the gaping mouths of the nestlings.

No one was more elated than John Bardsley and Councilman Smith when the house sparrows started to wage war on the caterpillars. Bardsley soon noticed a sharp decline in the number of inchworms in his garden. The results were the same in the other sections of the city where sparrows had been released. It was apparent to all that the English birds would and did eat American caterpillars.

Of course the sparrows did not eliminate all of the inchworms that first year—or the second year, for that matter. There were not enough birds to do the job. However, the sparrows adapted easily to their new habitat and multiplied rapidly. Five years after their importation, hardly an inchworm was to be seen in Philadelphia. Other cities also imported sparrows. New York, Buffalo, New Haven, Boston, and Portland, Maine, all put sparrows to work catching caterpillars. But no city imported as many of the birds as Philadelphia.

Philadelphians were content for a time. The green loopers no longer threatened the city's trees, thanks to the house sparrows. And citizens could now walk under a tree without being bombarded by inchworms. Even the skeptics conceded that John Bardsley—now nicknamed "Sparrow Jack"—had solved the inchworm problem.

Then something unexpected happened. Inchworms were still scarce; the sparrows saw to that. But another caterpillar started to appear on Philadelphia's trees and shrubs. It was the larva of the rusty vaporer moth, a yellow caterpillar with hairy bristles on its body.

When the vaporer moth caterpillars began to strip the leaves off trees, people looked to the sparrows for help. But the birds did not oblige this time. Neither they nor any other birds cared to eat the prickly caterpillars.

Naturally, the people of Philadelphia were disappointed with the sparrows, but some naturalists and other scientists went even further. They blamed the sparrows for the appearance of the vaporer moth caterpillars. The sparrows, claimed the scientists, had upset the balance of Nature.

Was this true?

Well, vaporer moth caterpillars emerged later in the spring than inchworms. Before the sparrows arrived in Philadelphia and other cities, vaporer moth caterpillars came out of their cocoons to find that the inchworms had eaten most of the food supply. As a result, many vaporer moth caterpillars died from starvation. The inchworms, then, had kept the other caterpillars in check.

The scientists argued that the house sparrows had removed this check by eliminating the inchworms. The vaporer moth caterpillars no longer faced a food shortage each year. Plenty of buds and leaves awaited them when they emerged in the late spring and early summer. And since no birds would eat them, the vaporer moth caterpillars increased year after year.

Unhappily, the new caterpillar invasion was only one of the complaints to be lodged against the sparrows. The doughty birds had adapted to their New World environment in an amazing manner. They produced brood after brood of nestlings. A decade after their importation in the northeastern United States, house sparrows were familiar birds in most cities and towns. While other birds preferred the wilderness or rural areas, the sparrows obviously thrived in urban centers.

As the sparrows increased in numbers, their popularity soon decreased. People grew tired of the little "brown birds," particularly people in the cities. Many now regarded the sparrows as pests. The little birds clustered on buildings and usurped the city streets. They were accused of driving songbirds away and ruining fruit tree buds. Philadelphia citizens who had once begged for relief from the inchworms now demanded relief from the sparrows. "Deliver us from our friends!" was their cry.

Some persons blamed Bardsley for introducing a threat worse than the inchworm. They accused him and others who had imported house sparrows of opening a Pandora's box. (Pandora, you may recall, was given a special box by the Greek god Zeus and was warned never to open it. But she became so curious that she ignored the warning and opened the box. Out popped all kinds of evil to flood the world. Only Hope remained inside.) The sparrow critics pointed to the vaporer moth caterpillar as an example of a released evil. And they claimed that the sparrows themselves had turned out to be an evil also.

It was true that the sparrows had not destroyed the vaporer moth caterpillars. But they had reduced the inchworms to a point where the little loopers were no longer a major problem. Most people, however, seemed to have forgotten that the house sparrows had saved countless valuable trees from the inchworms.

Nobody thought the house sparrows would adapt and multiply so rapidly. Bardsley was just as surprised as other people at the yearly increase in sparrows. He had expected the birds to survive and multiply to a certain extent, but he never dreamed that they would become the most numerous birds in North America.

By the end of the nineteenth century, house sparrows were found in almost every city and town in the United States. The little birds had even moved into southern Canada. There were several reasons for the population explosion of the sparrows. Other cities, taking a lesson from Philadelphia, Boston, and New York, had also imported the sparrows to fight insects. As the sparrow populations increased, the birds spread out from cities. They widened their range in the United States, fanning out in all directions.

The survival and spread of the house sparrows were a result of their character and habits. Man gave them a helping hand, but the sparrows had the ability to capitalize on that help. They were very unusual birds, as we shall learn.

CHAPTER TWO

The House Sparrow Is a Weaverbird

Many years ago, I made my first visit to Sparrow Jack's house in Germantown. Since that time I have studied the house sparrows in the city and suburbs. In fact, the house sparrow was one of the first birds that I learned about while earning the Bird Study Merit Badge. I lived in Philadelphia, so it was only natural that I should start with this sparrow—it was our most common species. I had but to go out on the street or gaze out a window and there was my bird.

The first fact I learned about it was that its common name was house sparrow. Americans probably slipped into the habit of calling these birds English sparrows because most of the imported birds came from England. However, some sparrows also came from France and Germany.

Next, I discovered that the house sparrow belonged to the Order *Passeriformes* (Passer-i-FOR-meez) and was a member of the family known as the *Ploceidae* (Plo-SEE-i-dee). What did all this mean? Well, all birds belong to an Order and Family. Some are even subdivided into Subfamilies and Tribes. To distinguish birds from other animals, scientists place them in a Class, *Aves* (AYE-veez). Then, to separate birds within the Class, ornithologists use another grouping: the Order. All birds in a specific Order have some common characteristics. The house sparrow's Order, *Passeriformes,* is composed of perching birds. All of these birds perch on or clutch twigs or branches when at rest.

Sparrows perch, but so do crows. Yet a sparrow and crow are not identical birds. Thus, another grouping is needed to distinguish birds within an Order. And that grouping is the Family. In the house sparrow's case, the family is the *Ploceidae,* or birds with conical beaks and other common traits. A further breakdown within the Family brings us to the *genus* (GEE-nus) and *species* (or in the case of some birds, subspecies). The genus tells us that the birds in that classification closely resemble one another. And we use the species (or subspecies) to identify an individual bird within the genus.

Now, if we let the house sparrow perch on his proper family tree, we can classify him as follows:

Class—*Aves*
Order—*Passeriformes*
Family—*Ploceidae*
Genus—*Passer* (first letter is always capitalized for genus)
Species—*domesticus*

Why is it necessary to have all these Latin or scientific names for the house sparrow? The answer is accuracy. Most people call the house sparrow an English sparrow. This can be confusing. But scientists all over the world know that *Passer domesticus* is one particular bird.

Let us return to the house sparrow's Order. It is a very large Order. About 5,100 of the more than 8,000 known species of birds are perching birds.

They all have four toes that are on the same level, and the toes are never webbed. The single hind toe is as long as the middle front toe. It helps these birds to grasp or perch. Also, the tail has twelve feathers.

The *Ploceidae* Family is made up of 136 species of perching birds. All are distributed within three groups: true sparrows (song, field, chipping, etc.), weaverbirds, and widow birds. The house sparrow is a weaverbird.

I learned that the three *Ploceidae* groups resembled the finches or *Fringillidae* (Frin-JIL-i-dee). Sparrows, weaverbirds, widow birds and finches (for example, canaries and goldfinches) all have conical beaks. All of them eat seeds and grains. And all of them will eat insects at certain times.

The house sparrow's relatives, the weaverbirds, are an interesting group. They are social birds that gather in flocks. Some live together in communal or apartment-house nests. Hundreds of weaverbirds join in to build these multifamily nests. When viewed from afar, the large structures look like thatched roofs hanging from a tree. Close up, one can see the holes through which the weaverbirds dart in and out. The *Quelea*—a weaverbird of East Africa —lives in one of these community nests which is so large that it sometimes spreads over an entire tree.

A close relative of the house sparrow, the widow bird, does not even bother to build a nest. It lays its eggs in nests of other birds. Then it flies off and— like the cowbird—leaves the job of incubating the eggs and rearing the young to the foster bird parents.

Weaverbirds are found throughout Africa, but only two species, the house sparrow and Eurasian tree sparrow, are native to Europe. The house sparrow's range originally included Palearctic Eurasia, North Africa, the British Isles eastward through Europe to central Siberia, India and Ceylon. In modern times, though, the house sparrow has a much wider range. The birds now inhabit Australia, New Zealand, Hawaii, North America, and temperate regions of South America and South Africa, as well as Europe and Asia.

Shortly after being introduced into North America, the house sparrow spread rapidly. Today, the birds are permanent residents in British Columbia, northern Manitoba, and northern Quebec, and their range extends southward in the West to Baja California and northern Mexico, and southward in the East to the Florida Keys.

This little bird's common surname—sparrow—stems from one of its characteristics. Watch a sparrow fly; it seems to flutter through the air. The old Teutonic word, *sparwa,* means a flutterer, and our English word, sparrow, is derived from it. Some other languages retain the Teutonic root word for sparrow. For example, a sparrow is known as a *sparf* in Sweden. In Germany, it is called a *sperling.* The Danes call a sparrow a *spurv.* A few languages use the bird's scientific name as a basis. Thus, the French know the sparrow as *le passereau.*

The house part of the sparrow's name also comes from a habit or trait of the bird. Sparrows live close to man, preferring crowded cities to open fields or forests. City houses and buildings substitute for trees, and sparrows will place their nests on any part of them. One may even find a sparrow nest on a window sill or behind a rainspout.

Only the house sparrow is found in cities and towns; its nearest relative, the Eurasian tree sparrow, prefers the fringes of cities and the countryside.

Although many people see house sparrows every day, few can accurately describe them. These persons see without observing. I have asked a number of persons to describe a house sparrow. Some actually mentioned color, but most simply stated that the sparrows were small, brownish birds. To be sure, house sparrows do have a brown color, but this is only a partial description. Furthermore, it fits many birds, including other sparrows.

This inability to describe house sparrows is not limited to novice bird watchers. I have met "old-timers" who stumble over the description; some dismiss the matter by saying that everybody knows the house sparrow. In addition, not all of the bird books or guides give a complete description of house sparrows. I remember how, after observing some sparrows, I searched among my bird books for one. I found only a brief mention of the birds. There were some terse notes, such as "House sparrow: too well known for description" and "Too common to be described."

House sparrows are more than mere "brown birds." Granted, that may be one's first impression upon seeing a city sparrow. But these street urchins do not show their true colors. They wear a sooty coat. Grime is a price the sparrows pay for living in or around man's habitats.

Leave the dusty city and go into the country.

There you will see a remarkable change in the colors of the house sparrows. Out beyond the pollution of the city, you will discover the birds cloaked in brighter colors. In fact, when you first see a country sparrow, you may think you have found a new or rare species of bird.

Many beginning bird watchers make this mistake. I did myself when I first went into the country. The house sparrows that I knew best were the soiled birds of Philadelphia's streets that I saw every day, month after month and year after year. It was difficult to detect any color on the little birds except a drab brown or gray, depending on the kind of dust that covered them. I just knew they were house sparrows.

Then I hiked into the country surrounding Philadelphia. On my first trip, I sighted small birds perching on or flying down from a barn. I was sure that they were some kind of sparrow. But when the sunlight bounced off their feathers, there were flashes of bright chestnut and pure white colors. My sparrows of the city streets had no such colors.

I considered the possibility of the birds being

chipping sparrows. Thumbing hastily through my bird guide, I searched for a description or color plate of the chipping sparrow. I found it, but saw that the birds around the barn were not chippies. Then I turned to a color plate of a house sparrow. The truth became apparent: the chestnut and white birds were ordinary house sparrows. They were just cleaner than their city kin.

The house sparrow, when observed in the right light and devoid of grime, is really a handsome bird. As with most birds, the males are more colorful than females. The male's upper parts are a vivid chestnut-brown. The top of the head, neck, lower back, rump, and tail coverts are ash-gray. A close look will reveal a black chin, throat, and lores. The cheeks and sides of the neck are white. When folded, the wings are chestnut-brown, with the middle coverts marked with a broad white band. The tail is dark brown, bordered with a pale chestnut color. House sparrows have brown eyes and reddish feet.

Females are dingy by comparison with the males. They do not have any black on the throat and face,

MALE

FEMALE

but their wings do have white wing bands. The head and neck of a female are ash-colored, tinged with brown. Most of the female's body is reddish-gray. Both male and female are small, stocky birds, ranging in size from five-and-a-quarter to six inches.

House sparrows with all-white tails or wings are not unusual. I have seen a number of them liberally marked with white. Again, when I first saw one of these "white" sparrows, I was confused and thought it to be another species. However, a thorough inspection through high-powered binoculars proved the bird to be just a house sparrow with more than its share of white.

There are more beautiful birds than the house sparrow. The little weaverbird is no match for the brilliant painted bunting or Baltimore oriole. He is a street gamin; sooty, grimy, and unkempt. But few other birds are as resourceful or as clever.

CHAPTER THREE

Sparrows in the Old World

Nobody really knows how long the house sparrows have lived in Europe and Asia, but we are quite sure that they were there at the first moment of recorded history. Their images appear in hieroglyphics carved by ancient peoples.

And they are most certainly there today. *Passer domesticus* chirps merrily from rooftops, barns, and trees in England, Scotland, Ireland, France, Spain, Portugal, Italy, Germany, the Netherlands, Scandinavia, eastern Asia, and parts of North Africa. The bold little birds are a very familiar sight to most Europeans and East Asians.

The Old World sparrows have met with both protection and persecution through the centuries. When they destroyed harmful insects, farmers and horticulturists hailed them as saviors. After the insect-uprisings were put down and the sparrows switched to a grain diet, agriculturists denounced them. Those who had benefited from the birds then turned around and killed them. Wholesale slaughter of sparrows has been common throughout Europe.

All kinds of inducements were found to promote the destruction of sparrows. Some provinces and countries offered bounties for dead sparrows. Others ordered their citizens or subjects to kill them. In Brandenburg (now a part of West Germany), the house sparrows had few friends in the eighteenth century. A royal fiat compelled peasants to capture or kill a certain number of the birds each year. Failure to bring in the prescribed number meant facing a fine or imprisonment.

The sparrows were ruthlessly hunted, but it was

not easy for all the peasants to fill their quotas. The house sparrows of yesterday were just as wary as those of today. Many peasants spent the night searching for sparrows. A few of the more prosperous farm-

ers hired professional sparrow hunters to help them obtain the required number.

These hunters (in Old High German they were known as *sparwari;* in modern German, they are

called *sperbers*) used various methods for catching and killing sparrows. Hundreds of the birds were trapped, shot, and poisoned. Altogether, the combined hunting methods of the sparrow hunters and peasants kept the sparrow population down.

But the wholesale destruction of the sparrows usually had severe repercussions. The mass slaughter of the birds was invariably followed by an upsurge in the insect population. This fact was clearly demonstrated in France during the eighteenth and nineteenth centuries.

Convinced that sparrows were destroying their fruit and grain, French farmers and fruitgrowers hired young boys to go into the fields and orchards, armed with nets and clubs. Thousands of birds were killed. Soon they became so scarce in many French agricultural regions that they could no longer be called common birds.

Now that the sparrows were so few, French agriculturists expected unusual grain and fruit harvests. But they had killed their best ally. Into the fields and onto the grain crops marched armies of beetles and other pests. A steady stream of caterpillars flowed over the branches and leaves of fruit trees. The invading insects went almost unmolested, for the one bird that could have kept them in check was no longer present in sufficient numbers. Instead of high grain and fruit yields, many French farmers and horticulturists were lucky to market any crops at all.

French agriculturists could not understand why the insect plagues descended on their crops. Few of them had ever paused to watch a pair of house sparrows feed their nestlings. None realized that the house sparrows ate the very insects that ruined the grain and fruit crops. Eventually, some Frenchmen remembered that they had little trouble with caterpillars and other insects when the sparrows were around. The truth finally came to them: it was the house sparrow that had kept the grain and fruit crops free from the insects.

This revelation was of little immediate comfort or benefit to the French farmers and fruitgrowers. They had been too thorough in their war with the sparrows, and the birds were all but wiped out. Those few that remained could hardly be expected to control the thousands of caterpillars, weevils, beetles, and bugs attacking the grain and fruit crops.

For many years, French farmers unsuccessfully battled the hordes of insects. Then the sparrows began to come back again. Slowly the little birds built up their numbers, and once more barnyards, fields, and orchards echoed with their chirping. After the sparrows' return, caterpillars and other harmful fruit and grain pests no longer posed a major threat to French agriculture. It had taken years, and serious financial setbacks, but the farmers had learned a lesson. In many parts of France, the house sparrow—*le passereau*—was no longer an enemy, but a friend.

The house sparrow suffered a similar fate in other European countries. In each instance, the farmers learned by bitter experience that the sparrows, despite their fondness for grain and fruit buds, were valuable birds. Many European farmers became convinced that it was better to lose a little grain and fruit to the sparrows than to lose all to the insects.

European farms and orchards were not the only places where the house sparrows met with difficulty. They had enemies in Old World cities too. City dwellers complained that the sparrows were noisy, messy, and impudent birds. Furthermore, bird lovers maintained that whenever a family of sparrows moved into a garden, they drove out the wrens, finches, and thrushes.

In England, the house sparrows faced criticism in both town and country. Amateur and professional agriculturists and naturalists debated the advantages and disadvantages of the little birds. Champions of the sparrows fed and protected the birds whenever possible, while dedicated sparrow-haters killed any that came under their traps or gun sights.

Thomas Bewick, who made the engravings for the celebrated book, *A History of British Birds,* spoke up for the sparrows. "In the destruction of caterpillars," wrote Bewick, "the sparrows are eminently serviceable to vegetation—and in this respect alone, there is reason to suppose that they sufficiently repay the destruction they may make in the produce garden or field."

Other friends of the sparrows spoke or wrote their approval of the birds, emphasizing the sparrow's value to farmers. As for the house sparrows congregating around city and country houses—well, the residents benefited by that too. The sparrows caught flies that buzzed about house and barn. If it weren't for the hungry birds, the flies would soon multiply to an intolerable degree.

Supporters of the sparrows also argued that both amateur and professional gardeners ought to be thankful that the sparrows lived in or visited their gardens. The birds were enemies of cabbage butterflies, whose larvae caused great destruction. Without the aid of the house sparrows, it was doubtful whether cabbage plants would thrive in England.

For each friend of the sparrows, though, there were dozens of enemies. Some of the latter went to unusual lengths to condemn the house sparrows. They lectured and wrote against the birds. Their arguments included the accusation that the sparrows had been man's enemies for nearly 3,000 years. As evidence, the foes of the sparrows stated that when writing was invented, the sparrow was chosen as the hieroglyph which meant enemy.

What with all the wars that were fought against the sparrows in Europe, it is a wonder the birds did not become extinct. At times their numbers did fall to dangerous lows, but whenever they were given a respite, the sparrows managed to come back again. Then they would multiply, and once more European cities and farms would resound with their lively chirps.

CHAPTER FOUR

House Sparrows in America

No other bird immigrant to North America became so thoroughly established in so short a time as did the house sparrow. In fact, the sparrow's adaptation to its new environment was unparalleled in the history of any bird.

To a large extent, the success of the sparrows in America can be traced to the character of the birds themselves. Tough, resourceful, and bold, they thrive where other species cannot. Sparrows can endure both tropical heat and subarctic cold. North America, with its varied climatic zones, offered the birds almost ideal conditions.

John Bardsley and others who imported the sparrows saw to it that they received a good start in the New World. In the beginning, they were carefully protected. But more important, the sparrows found plenty of food and nesting sites. Competition from other birds was not nearly so keen as it had been in the Old World.

Another major factor in the quick spread of the birds was their tameness. Many immigrants from Europe brought pet sparrows with them to the cities of North America. A sparrow "craze" or fad resulted,

and it prevailed in most of the United States at the turn of the century. More and more people wanted house sparrows as pets. While the demand lasted, sparrow importers conducted a profitable business.

Pet sparrows frequently escaped from their cages

or pens. Most of them became semiwild birds, living in the cities and suburbs. They mated, built nests, and raised nestlings to swell the sparrow population. The population peak was reached at the end of the last century. From that time and into the first two decades of this century, house sparrows undoubtedly were the most abundant birds on the continent.

Ultimately, the sparrow population leveled off, then gradually declined. In those regions where the sparrows enjoyed relative protection, the population remained stable. But disease, severe weather, and predators killed off large numbers of the sparrows in other parts of the country.

The spread of the internal combustion engine also contributed to the decline of sparrows. Tractors and trucks displaced horses in the city and on the farm. Less horses meant less grain grown for feed. Many city sparrows had shared oats and other grains spilled by livery horses, milkwagon horses, fire horses, draft horses, and even pleasure horses. With the horses gone and the grain supply all but shut off, countless city sparrows died of starvation.

Perhaps the most important factor in the sparrows' decline, though, was the change in the American people's attitude toward them. When they first arrived in Philadelphia, the birds were hailed for ridding that city's trees of inchworms. But after it was discovered that they would not eat other harmful insects, public sentiment turned against them. The same thing happened in other cities during the latter part of the nineteenth century, and the sparrows that once were so carefully nurtured now became outcasts.

H. A. Purdie, a prominent Bostonian and a leader of the "anti-sparrow" movement, wrote to a Boston newspaper in 1877: "Why these caterpillars on our trees? With more sparrows than ever before, how can it be? These crawling things (caterpillars) come from eggs that all last Fall, Winter, and Spring the pretty little sparrows should have eaten. The eggs were laid by the wingless imago, which should have been devoured. The chrysalis must now be swallowed as a dainty morsel. But no! Not one is molested by *Passer domesticus!*"

Dr. Elliot Coues, the noted historian and ornithologist, had some especially harsh words for house sparrows. Coues, in addition to his research and writing in ornithology, edited the journals of the Lewis and Clark Expedition.

"*Passer domesticus,*" wrote Dr. Coues in 1886, "was introduced some years ago. Now these rowdy little gamins squeak and fight all through the city to our great disgust." He charged that the sparrows interfered with the balance of power among native species, and contended that they molested, harassed, maltreated, and forcibly ejected various birds. Coues concluded his condemnation of the sparrows by stating that they deprived other birds of "certain inalienable rights to life, liberty and the pursuit of happiness after their own fashion."

These were strong words from the distinguished historian and ornithologist, but they indicated some of the hard feelings that were building up against the sparrows. In fact, so hostile were these feelings that it was suggested the sparrows be denied any protection. When the American Ornithologists' Union and Audubon Societies proposed a "Model Bird Law" for adoption by the states, the views of the sparrows' enemies prevailed. Passed in 1886, the law offered protection to songbirds and other nongame birds, but "exempted house sparrows; their eggs and nests from any protection or consideration whatsoever."

Thomas Gentry, naturalist and author of *Life Histories of Birds of Eastern Pennsylvania,* did not think much of the sparrows, either. Gentry had witnessed the build-up of house sparrows in Philadelphia, most of which had come from Bardsley's original stock. In Gentry's opinion, the sparrows were out of place in America and existed under unnatural conditions. Furthermore, he claimed, the birds could no longer be depended upon to keep insects in check. The sparrows were being spoiled—they found it easier to eat scraps from the street and grain from the fields and barnyards.

Gentry suggested that if the sparrows were not to

be killed off, then they should be forced to shift for themselves. People ought to stop tossing grain and other food to the birds. Garbage and trash can lids should fit tightly. Then, declared Gentry, the pampered sparrows might change their sinful ways. Pressed by hunger and in danger of starvation, the birds would have to search for their food. They would probe the fissured bark of trees, and any lurking beetles, hidden chrysalises, or insect eggs would be picked out and eaten. If all this happened, Gentry said, then the sparrows again could be considered useful birds.

Fortunately, the house sparrows in America, like those in the Old World, were not without friends. One of them was Dr. Thomas Mayo Brewer, another celebrated ornithologist. Brewer was an oölogist; his special interest in ornithology was the study of bird eggs. He was a friend of John J. Audubon and furnished information on birds for Audubon's monumental work, *Birds of America*. Two species of birds were named in honor of Dr. Brewer. They are known today as Brewer's blackbird and Brewer's sparrow.

Brewer publicly defended the house sparrows. In his estimation, they did a great deal of good. Thousands of dollars would not pay the city of Boston for the loss of its house sparrows, Brewer declared. While the birds did not destroy the vaporer moth caterpillar, they did consume large quantities of other harmful insects.

Dr. Brewer also urged American farmers and horticulturists to pay heed to what had happened in Europe when the house sparrows were slaughtered. It would be disastrous, he said, to kill off the birds and rely on native species to keep insects in check. "Those birds on the protected lists, the favorite songbirds of the garden—often called useful birds—actually do very little in comparison with the sparrows as to the destruction of harmful insects."

Despite the support of men like Dr. Brewer, the war against the house sparrows went on and on. City dwellers accused the sparrows of carrying diseases. Admittedly the little birds were dirty, and they did come into contact with garbage and other refuse. But so did other birds. Nobody had ever proved that the house sparrows actually spread disease. Still, the possibility was there and it provided enough ammunition for the sparrow-haters.

In the first ten years of the twentieth century, the house sparrows came under even stronger persecution. Their chief opponents, as usual, were farmers and horticulturists who called on the federal government to set up controls to reduce the house sparrow population.

Accordingly, the United States Government launched a study of the house sparrow and its destructive ways. The task was given to the Bureau of Biological Survey, the forerunner of our present Bureau of Sport Fisheries and Wildlife. Ned Dearborn, a biologist with the Bureau, wrote a booklet on the results of the sparrow study. It was issued in 1910 as *Farmer's Bulletin Number 383* under the aegis of the United States Department of Agriculture.

This bulletin itemized the house sparrow's sins:

The bird had no special appeal. It lacked musical talent; in fact, had no song. House sparrows were known to be public nuisances in the cities. And, of course, the bulletin made the customary accusation that the sparrows destroyed grain and fruit crops.

Not surprisingly, the sin that carried the most weight with the Department of Agriculture was that of destroying crops. Agriculture was a major part of the American economy. If house sparrows were its enemies, then it followed that they were enemies of the American people too. In 1912, the United States Department of Agriculture issued a revised edition of Ned Dearborn's 1910 bulletin. It contained a new section: How to trap and kill house sparrows.

It is difficult to believe that the house sparrows ever posed such a threat to America's bountiful grain and fruit production as to deserve unrestricted killing. Yet this was the judgment and sentence passed on them. No other birds, except the hawks, have ever been so systematically persecuted. And ironically enough, both sparrows and hawks are really the farmer's friends.

Time has not changed the status of the house sparrows. They are still outlaws. Luckily the birds no longer undergo wholesale slaughter. True, they are not on the protected bird list and there is a permanent open season on them. But today the killing of sparrows is an occasional event, and only a few of them are likely to be killed at a time.

City sparrows enjoy a relative immunity from persecution. Now and then municipal authorities try to discourage them from congregating on public buildings, usually without much success. Airports trap sparrows—and other birds—because of their threat to planes, especially jets, taking off and landing. Sparrows and starlings have sometimes been sucked into jet engines, causing considerable damage.

Other than a few of these emergency control measures, though, house sparrows receive no special attention. They hop about city streets or chirp merrily from a rooftop—noticed by a few people, ignored by most. Each day, hundreds of cities and towns awaken to the gay twittering of house sparrows. An old lady, confined to a room, opens a window and throws a handful of bread crusts to the house sparrows out-side. A boy watches a sparrow and pigeon tussle over a kernel of corn in a city park. Five baby sparrows thrust their opened beaks out of a nest, and a small girl stares at them, wide-eyed.

Yes, the house sparrows are urchins of the city. But the birds are also a vital part of a city's pulse; noisy, irregular, but necessary.

CHAPTER FIVE

The Ways of Sparrows

Thomas Bewick, the noted British engraver and naturalist, once said: "The house sparrow follows Society and lives at its expense." There is no question that the house sparrows prefer civilization to the wilderness. Rooftops and streets appeal to them more than trees and meadows. And by electing to live in the cities, the house sparrows actually strengthen their chances of survival.

As habitats for birds, most cities are relatively unexploited. The house sparrows, along with starlings, pigeons, mockingbirds, and blue jays, live almost unchallenged. Competition for food and nesting sites is minimal. Just consider the food sources in your own city or town: hundreds of ornamental trees and shrubs, trash cans from every house, occasional bird feeders—these are only some of the food suppliers for the house sparrows. As for nesting sites, the sparrows find more than they can use. When we reflect on these advantages, there is no mystery as to why the house sparrows have not only survived, but multiplied in great numbers. Their city habitat is good to them.

House sparrows are social birds. They gather in small flocks on buildings, fences, and city streets. Observe a group of them feeding in the street or back yard. The birds hop and dart about while searching for food. Some push and shove each other. A din of chirps rises up as the sparrows go after a crust of bread or handful of scattered grain. Noisy, quarrelsome, and dauntless, they are the underdogs of the bird world.

When food is plentiful, the sparrows feed in harmony. But let there be a scarcity, and fighting breaks out. House sparrows are no better or worse than other birds in this respect. Hunger is a powerful force among all living creatures, including man.

House sparrows have been called impudent birds. I suppose that this is so. But impudence is part of their nature and a trait that has helped to keep them alive. While the sparrows show boldness on occasion, they are not foolish. They take few chances. Even though a flock of them may seem occupied with arguments, the birds are almost always alert to danger. Let a cat, dog, or person approach too close, and up and away fly the sparrows. Tame though they may be, they are not so stupid as to allow their tameness to endanger them.

When taking flight, the sparrows do not all rise up together, as do some ducks and other birds. Only a part of the flock takes to the air, usually those birds closest to the peril. The others remain behind, picking up morsels of food, but with an eye on the danger. Then, just when it seems these daring birds will be caught, they take flight too. Usually, sparrows do not fly far away; they move just far enough to be out of the way of trouble.

The flight of sparrows is not impressive. A house sparrow does not fly with the grace of a whistling swan or the speed of a falcon. It is an awkward and slow flyer. Nevertheless, what flying power the sparrow does have is adequate for the bird's needs.

The house sparrow's flight is direct, propelling the bird where it wants to go. There is no hovering or circling about. The sparrow simply selects a place to go and then flies there in an irregular path. Short, stubby wings beat firmly, whisking the sparrow

along. The bird rarely flies high and does not migrate, at least not for any great distances.

Regretfully, the sparrow's slow flight renders him open to attack by swifter birds. Blue jays, mockingbirds, grackles, and starlings can outfly a house sparrow, and these birds often rout the smaller species. Sparrows in turn often join together to drive birds smaller and more timid than themselves from a territory.

House sparrows have few natural enemies. But the birds must always keep vigilant against air raids by hawks and ground attacks by cats and weasels.

Sparrows unite in a common strategy when a hawk threatens them. If a sparrow sees a hawk shadow— or the hawk itself—the bird gives an alarm. Then all of the sparrows in the neighborhood join in with loud chirps and twitterings. The sparrows know they cannot win in a race with a hawk. But they do seem to know that a hawk cannot catch all of them. Therefore, the sparrows fly in different directions, still sounding their chirps. This scattering and chirping confuses the hawk. He doesn't know which sparrow to chase. While he is making up his mind, the sparrows dash to the safety of a house or tree.

House sparrows sound lively and discordant calls when they are irritated. If he is merely annoyed, the bird will utter a loud *twi-twi-twoo, twi-twi-twoo.* These calls often come out in rapid-fire style. An angry sparrow emits a sharp *twi-che!*

The house sparrow is no musical virtuoso. He does not even have a song. His musical efforts consist solely of a series of monotonous chirps. But despite his very limited musical talents, the house sparrow engages in considerable vocalizing. When courting, a male sparrow chirps loudly and sometimes with incredible speed. I once timed a courting male's delivery of chirps: he obliged with 105 a minute!

A flock of house sparrows often indulges in what we might call a chirping chorus. This event generally takes place in early evening. All of the birds chirp at one time, and their noise—it can scarcely be called music—is loud and out of tune. Each sparrow seems determined to outchirp his comrades. There is a gradual rise in the pitch and loudness of this communal chirping. It may last as long as a half hour, then will stop suddenly. I have never learned why the sparrows engage in this communal chirping —perhaps, since they are social birds, they just like to gather and chirp.

I have listened to sparrows chirping from my porch, rooftop, and apple trees, and their twittering has awakened me in the early morning. Even now, as I write, a dozen of them twit and chirp as they peck at seed pods on a large mimosa tree outside my study window. For me the chirping of the house sparrows is a pleasant sound; yet I know persons who strongly object to it. This has puzzled me. Surely the noises of the city are more irksome than the twitterings of sparrows. I find it much more pleasant to be awakened on a dreary morning by the chirps of cheerful sparrows, than to wake up with no bird calls at all.

But let us return to the group chirping of the house sparrows. On more than one occasion I have noticed an interesting thing happen during an evening chirp-fest. It occurs near the end of the period. One house sparrow, after having chirped loudly for a half hour or so, will suddenly sound a very sharp note. This note is different from the customary chirp. It sounds more like *twit!* and seems to be both a signal and command to end the chirping program. And I have noticed that every sparrow instantly obeys the order.

In winter, when other birds are stilled, the house sparrow keeps right on chirping. One blustery March day, a sparrow hunched down on a naked branch of an apple tree in my garden. The sharp wind shook the tree and ruffled the sparrow's feathers. He clung desperately to the branch, chirping all the while. At least that is what I supposed he was doing, for his beak kept opening and closing. Although I stood within ten feet of the bird, I could hear no sound except the whining of the wind. I waited, and finally there was a lull in the wind's gusts. At last I heard some of the sparrow's valiant, if feeble, chirps.

House sparrows mate in early spring. The specific time varies slightly in North America, depending upon the region. In the South, the mating urge comes on the sparrows in March. Canadian sparrows mate and nest in early May. In between—throughout the intermediate zones—mating and nesting usually occur in April.

Mating time brings on a spurt of activity in the sparrow community and many heated contests. Males joust with each other, calling loudly, crouching, and then bobbing up and down, wings outstretched. Some males form a "dancing" ring around a desirable female. This animated ring is a circle of male sparrows all strutting and bobbing at once. Soon there are fights, with the males pecking and biting each other. All during the courtship, the area resounds with chirping and twittering. Finally mates are chosen and the pairs of birds hurry off to a nesting site. House sparrows, unlike eagles and swans, do not mate for life. They usually choose a new mate each year.

Both male and female share the task of building the nest. The male collects nesting materials—string, straw, feathers, cloth, dried grass; in fact, almost anything that holds together. The female weaves the materials into a nest.

A pair of sparrows may spend five to six days building their nest. Some sparrows will utilize an old nest, rather than build a new one. I have known sparrows to occupy the same nest for several seasons, abandoning it only when the structure fell apart.

The house sparrow's nest is no work of art. It is usually a coarse structure, lacking the delicacy of a Baltimore oriole's hanging nest, for example. But it more than serves the purpose for which it is intended; namely, to hold eggs and nestlings. House sparrow nests vary in size. The inside of an average-sized nest, where the eggs are laid and nestlings live, measures about three inches wide at the top and about two inches deep.

House sparrows are not particular as to where they place their nests. A nest may be located anywhere that materials can be arranged and held fast. Rooftops, eaves, rain-gutters, holes, ledges, decayed trees, and even mailboxes serve as nesting sites.

Sometimes house sparrows will usurp the nest of another species. This piracy is one reason why the house sparrow is an unwelcome bird. House sparrows will also—when allowed—build their nests on top of, or adjacent to, those of large birds. Naturally the bird-landlords must be friendly. For example, storks permit house sparrows to set up housekeeping atop their own huge nests. I don't think this sharing of nest sites is true *mutualism*—a situation where two different species live together for mutual benefit. More than likely, the storks merely tolerate the house sparrows and their nest.

Occasionally, a pair of house sparrows will erect their nest in an unusual place. I remember a sparrow nest on top of an arc light over a busy city street. The bright light and traffic noise did not seem to bother the birds. They attended to the business of rearing nestlings with the same calmness they would have shown if their nest had been hidden in a thicket.

Imagine a sparrow nest in the rigging of an old sailing ship. Years ago, when the sailing vessel *Great Britain* lay in dock, a pair of nautical-minded house sparrows built their nest in one of its furled sails. The nest remained intact during the ship's voyage to Scotland, but on the next trip, when the crew unfurled the sail, it was unfortunately lost.

Some house sparrows once built a nest in the rotunda of a Dublin, Ireland, building. The round room contained a beautiful carved frieze that portrayed heads of oxen, decorated with hanging flowers. This unusual animal frieze encircled the entire rotunda, rather high up from the floor. The sparrows placed their nest in the hollow of an ox eye.

Female house sparrows lay eggs at the rate of one each day until a clutch is reached. Usually, five or six eggs make up a clutch. The eggs may be white, greenish, or bluish, with tiny gray or brown spots on the ends. Several clutches are laid during a season.

The female sparrow sits on the eggs for ten to twelve days. Since the eggs are not all laid at one time, they do not hatch at the same time. But all fertile eggs generally hatch by the end of the twelve-day incubation period. While the male helps to build the nest, he does not share the incubation chore. He prefers the more masculine task of guarding the nest and eggs.

The male is extremely aggressive at nesting time, driving off any bird that dares come near the nest. The size of a would-be egg robber means nothing to the male sparrow. I have seen an indignant house sparrow chase a thieving blue jay out of the nesting territory.

When a raider appears, both the male and the female also send out loud calls for help. These calls quickly bring other sparrows to the rescue. The reinforcements mob and chase away the egg thieves with dive-bombing and pecks.

The rearing of two or three broods of sparrow nestlings each season is a big job. Both male and female are dedicated parents, working from dawn to nightfall to provide food for their offspring. Baby sparrows have large appetites and are fed exclusively on various insects and larvae. Caterpillars, grubs, Japanese beetles, aphids, weevils, earthworms, and flies are all greedily devoured by the nestlings. For the first few days, however, the parent birds predigest the food, then regurgitate it into the wide open mouths of the babies. Later, the nestlings eat whole insects.

Some species of birds abandon any nestlings that topple from the nest. But not the house sparrows.

The sparrow parents continue to feed any youngster that has fallen out of the nest. They also protect the displaced nestling, driving off any predatory bird, mammal, or reptile that tries to make a meal of the fallen sparrow.

The sparrow parents work very hard and burn

up a great deal of energy while raising their nestlings. Since they are so active, adult sparrows must eat frequently. They also have rapid heartbeats. However, the sparrow's body functions slow down at night, including the heartbeats. This is Nature's way of giving the birds a rest. If they did not get such a rest, the sparrows would have to eat all night long to keep up their energy.

Young house sparrows lack the bright plumage of the adults. Light brown and gray are the dominant colors of the young sparrows before their first molt, or shedding of feathers. Usually, immature house sparrows finish the first molt by winter. After that time, their feathers come in with richer hues. Young male sparrows acquire the deep chestnut color and black throat of their fathers, and immature females take on the drabber plumage of their mothers. However, both male and female youngsters display white wing bars.

Immature sparrows leave the nest when they are twelve or thirteen days old, but they do not go very far away. They remain near it while the parents feed them for another ten days. When this time is up, the young sparrows are weaned and seek their own food. House sparrow parents, unlike some other bird parents—notably hawks—do not drive half-grown youngsters out of the territory. Immature sparrows are permitted to live near the nesting site. I have observed a sparrow nest with week-old nestlings of a second brood inside, while perched nearby were members of the first brood. House sparrow parents recognize both new and old nestlings, by sight and by sound.

It is when they are feeding their young that the house sparrows perform a great service to farmers, gardeners, and horticulturists. A single adult sparrow can carry forty grubs an hour to the nest. The parent birds work about twelve hours a day, seven days a week, during the nestling season. One sparrow may catch as many as 3,000 grubs and other insects while feeding a brood. And of course the adult sparrows also eat insects while rearing nestlings. It is no wonder, then, that the house sparrows drastically reduced the inchworm population in Philadelphia in a relatively short time.

Once the last brood is out of the nest and seeking its own food, the diet of the sparrows undergoes a change. The birds switch from insects to seeds and grains. The change-over occurs toward the end of summer and continues through fall and winter. Included in this vegetarian diet are seeds of unwanted plants, such as dandelions, crab grass, and ragweed.

City sparrows, of course, do not have as many varieties of grains or insects to eat as country sparrows do. But the city sparrows manage to find different foods. In the spring and summer they eat insects and worms. Then in fall and winter they switch to weed and other plant seeds in back yards and empty lots, and to bread and other food dropped from garbage cans.

House sparrows will change their eating pattern when there is an outbreak of Japanese beetles, aphids, weevils, inchworms, or locusts. Often they eat nothing but insects during one of these plagues, even though they may have already started on a seed or grain diet. Nobody really knows why they switch. Perhaps the sparrows simply want a change in food. Regardless of the reason, this sudden change is a big help to farmers and city gardeners.

House sparrows are relentless insect hunters, pursuing beetles and other bugs in the air and on the ground. When chasing flying insects, the sparrows flutter like barn swallows, zigzagging this way and that. In pursuit of a grasshopper, the sparrows may spring like a road runner or even leapfrog after the insect. Once, during an unusual invasion of aphids, I saw sparrows hanging upside down on my rose bushes. Since I had seen the invasion of aphids, I knew what the sparrows were doing. They were searching for the pale-green aphids hidden under the leaves or clustered on the rose stems.

Even though they are what we might call part-time insect eaters, the house sparrows are useful birds. Moreover, they destroy a greater number of harmful insects than do many of the so-called useful birds. Yet the sparrows are not on any protected bird list. Instead, because they eat grain and disturb other birds, they are still regarded as outlaws.

House sparrows do eat grain and the amount lost represents an economic loss. But I have often wondered about this loss. Is it really greater than the gain brought about by the destruction of great numbers of harmful insects? I suspect that far more grain is lost or damaged by careless handling and storage than is eaten by sparrows.

House sparrows are interesting birds. Their choice

of the city as a place to live is fortunate, not only for them but for people who live in the city. City sparrows are all about us, providing us with bird life when there is no other.

CHAPTER SIX

Sparrows in Verse and Story

Poets, dramatists, and authors have used birds as themes or objects of comparison since ancient times. The virtues of elegant swans, majestic eagles, and melodious nightingales are praised in classical and modern literary works. When compared to these noteworthy birds, the house sparrows seem poor contenders for literary tributes. Yet the lowly sparrows have found their way into verse, play, and story.

No writer has written an ode to a house sparrow. Never has the bird been extolled as an example of power, beauty, or melody. This is understandable, for who would believe such praise? The bird is too ordinary to merit glorification. However, the low esteem in which the sparrows have often been held has appealed to some writers, who have used them as subjects for comparison. And other authors have pointed out that, although common and insignificant, the sparrow is still a living creature worthy of consideration.

The authors of the Bible did not neglect the sparrows. To be sure, we cannot say for certain that the sparrows mentioned in the Bible were *Passer domesticus*. It is possible that they were a close relative of the house sparrow, or a species known as *Passer moabiticus* (moab-IT-i-cus). Then, too, the Hebrew equivalent of the word sparrow is *tsippor*, which means birds in general, especially small ones. Regardless of which species of weaverbird appears in the Bible, the fact remains that sparrows were common in the Holy Land.

In Matthew 10:29, Jesus speaks to the disciples before sending them forth. Among other things, He instructs them with these words: "Are not two sparrows sold for a penny? And not one of them will fall to the ground without your Father's will. But even the hairs of your head are all numbered. Fear not, therefore; you are of more value than many sparrows."

There is this reference to the sparrow in Psalm 102:7: "I watch, and am as a sparrow alone upon the housetop."

Shakespeare drew comparisons of man and sparrow in his verse-plays. He wrote this about the sparrow in Act II, Scene 3, of *As You Like It:*

> *". . . and He that doth the ravens feed*
> *Yea, providently caters for the sparrow."*

What Shakespeare implies here is that God takes equal care of all living creatures, regardless of their position in life.

Again, the great English writer used a similar theme in *Hamlet* (Act V, Scene 2) when he wrote: "There's a special providence in the fall of a sparrow."

The death of a sparrow, he is saying, does not go unnoticed by God. The tragedy is attended with the same degree of pity and compassion as that accorded the death of an eagle or a king.

Alexander Pope, in his famous *Essay on Man,* also pursued this theme. Pope penned these words about the importance of a sparrow:

> *"Who sees with equal eye, as God of all,*
>   *A hero perish or a sparrow fall,*
>   *Atoms or systems into ruin hurl'd*
>   *And now a bubble bursts, and now a world."*

Even the sparrows themselves are concerned with the fall of one of them. In the 1880's, the *New York Sun* printed an item about a fallen sparrow. Their reporter had observed a flock of sparrows twittering excitedly in the Jersey City ferry house of the Pavonia Ferry. One of the sparrows huddled on the floor, sick or injured. The other birds hopped and chirped around their fallen comrade. It seemed as if they were trying to decide what to do about their wounded friend. The chirping became louder and louder, rising to a shrill crescendo. Then the sparrows nearest the victim pushed him, chirping all the while. Two birds tried to lift the fallen sparrow, each of them easing one of its wings under the wounded bird. A chorus of chirps from the other sparrows encouraged both the victim and rescuers.

Time after time, the sparrows tried to get their fallen friend into the air. They seemed to realize that he was in great danger on the floor. Nudging and lifting, the sparrows urged the wounded one to rise up. Several times he almost succeeded, and several times he and the others tumbled back to the floor of the ferry house. Then, as if all the sparrows had agreed on one last try, the birds pushed, lifted, and dragged the fallen sparrow to the top cornice of a pillar. There he was carefully set down and covered with bits of straw and feathers. Satisfied that their fallen comrade was now safe, all of the sparrows perched on a wire and celebrated the rescue with a loud chorus of chirps.

To return to the classics: William Cowper, the eighteenth century British poet, mentioned the sparrow's fondness for grain in this verse:

"The sparrows peep and quit the sheltering eaves
To seize the fair occasion; well they eye
The scattered grain, and thievishly resolve
To escape the impending famine . . ."

In his book, *Life Sings a Song,* Samuel Hoffenstein, the Lithuanian-born newspaperman, screen writer, and poet, expressed his admiration for the lowly sparrows:

"Of all the birds that sing and fly
Between the housetops and the sky
The muddy sparrows, mean and small
I like, by far, the best of all."

Hoffenstein, in the third line of this verse, refers to the sparrows as "mean and small." He did not intend the word *mean* to signify that sparrows are ignoble or bad-tempered birds. He used it in another sense: the sparrow's humbleness and lack of distinction.

The cleverness and resourcefulness of the sparrow are featured in an amusing poem by Arthur Guiterman, "The Universal Etiquette for Educated Cats":

> *"The Gossips tell a story of the Sparrow*
>   *and the Cat,*
> *The Feline thin and hungry and the Bird*
>   *exceeding fat.*
> *With eager, famished energy and claws of*
>   *gripping steel,*
> *Puss pounced upon the Sparrow and pre-*
>   *pared to make a meal.*

> *"The Sparrow never struggled when he*
>   *found that he was caught*
> *(If somewhat slow in action he was mighty*
>   *quick of thought)*

But chirped in simple dignity that seemed
    to fit the case:
'No Gentleman would ever eat before he'd
    washed his face!'

"This hint about his manners wounded
    Thomas like a knife
(For Cats are great observers of the Niceties
    of Life)
He paused to lick his paws, which seemed
    the Proper Thing to Do
And, chirruping derisively, away the Spar-
    row flew.

"In helpless, hopeless hunger at the Spar-
    row on the bough,
Poor Thomas glowered longingly, then
    vowed a Solemn Vow:
'Henceforth, I'll eat my dinner first, then
    wash myself!' and that's
The Universal Etiquette for Educated
    Cats."

The old nursery tale, "The Burial of Cock Robin," briefly presents the sparrow in the role of villain. It is told in this dialogue:

"Who killed Cock Robin?"
"I," said the Sparrow, "with my bow and arrow."

We are never told *why* the sparrow killed Cock Robin.

"A Tame Sparrow and His Ways" is the title of an anecdote written by the Reverend J. G. Wood and included in his book, *Man and Beast: Here and Hereafter,* published in 1874. The book is a fascinating collection of stories and accounts of animal and bird behavior. Unhappily, it is a rare book today and not readily available.

The sparrow in the Rev. Mr. Wood's story was rescued by an English lady's brother from some boys who had robbed a nest. The lady kept the sparrow in a small box. Later, when the bird got over its fright, she gave it the freedom of the house. There was a cat in the house, but she was watched carefully by the lady.

On Sundays, when the family attended church, the sparrow was put out in the garden. The cat remained inside. Despite the fact that he was free, the sparrow always stayed in the garden until the lady returned from church. The signal for his re-entry into the house was when the lady opened the dining-room window. But there was more to the signal: the lady had to stand at the window without her gloves. If she wore her gloves, the sparrow refused to come into the house. Apparently the Rev. Mr. Wood believed that the sparrow associated the gloves with the departure of the family for church. This would mean, of course, that the sparrow and cat would be left alone . . . and the sparrow would not be safe in the house.

Another anecdote in the Rev. Mr. Wood's book is called "Generosity in a Sparrow." An English lady kept a collection of cage birds, including a canary. On warm days, she hung the canary's cage just outside a window. One morning, a house sparrow flew to the cage and perched on top. He chirped to the canary a few times, then flew away.

Presently the sparrow returned to the canary's cage with a grub. He poked it through the bars and the canary quickly gobbled down the choice food. Every day at the same time the sparrow appeared with a grub, which he gave to the canary.

Eventually, the canary anticipated the sparrow's arrival by taking a position close to the cage bars. When the sparrow came with the daily offering, the canary took it directly from the sparrow's beak.

The lady was delighted with the sparrow's generosity. She placed other cages near that of the canary. In the cages were some finches and lovebirds. When the sparrow saw the additional cages, he doubled his energies to bring back food for all the birds. However, he always fed the canary first, and spent more time at the canary's cage than at the others. (The sparrow's interest in the canary is no mystery. The canary is a finch, and sparrows and finches have an affinity for each other.)

One more tale by the observant Rev. Mr. Wood is

worth retelling because it describes some interesting bird behavior. The story is called "A Sparrow
Usurps a Martins' Nest."

In the summer of 1849, a pair of martins built
their nest in an archway of the stables at Woburn
Abbey, Bedfordshire, England. They industriously
lined the nest with feathers and bits of cloth. A house
sparrow came along and alighted on it. He liked
what he saw and decided to take possession of the
nest. Of course, the martins objected to this high-
handed act. They tried to eject the sparrow, but
were unsuccessful. After several attempts, they gave
up and flew off.

The martins had by no means abandoned their
home to the nest-squatting sparrow, however. They
had merely gone for help. Shortly afterward, the
dispossessed martins returned with reinforcements.
Now thirty martins faced the sparrow. They dragged
him out of the nest and onto a grassy plot nearby.
All of the martins formed a circle around the sparrow. They eyed him for a few minutes, and then—
although there was no audible signal—all attacked

the sparrow at once. When the shrill cries of the enraged martins stopped, the sparrow was dead.

Now, this tale is not as fanciful as it may seem. Some birds do sit in collective judgment on a law-breaker. For example, the house crows of India often hold a circle court. The Hindus call it *Punchayeti*. The crows form a ring around the misdoer. All the crows keep quiet, as though they are deciding on the sentence. Meanwhile, the accused bird makes no attempt to escape during the trial. He remains in the center of the circle, quietly awaiting his fate.

Suddenly the conference is over. The ring of crows explodes into a blur of metallic black feathers as the judges-and-jury attack the culprit. Sometimes the victim is killed; often he is just given a beating. Perhaps the severity of the sentence depends upon the crime.

There is little about the house sparrows in contemporary literary works. This is regrettable, for these birds have interesting habits. But it may be that some boy or girl—gazing out the window at sparrows on a winter day or listening to a sparrow chirp-fest—will be inspired to write a poem or story about these ragamuffins of the city.

CHAPTER SEVEN

A Sparrow Watcher's Notes

Last summer, I revisited Sparrow Jack's house on Upsal Street in the Germantown section of Philadelphia. The house and street retain much of the charm they had in John Bardsley's day. I have seen nineteenth century drawings of the house and it has undergone little alteration. On this particular trip, I saw house sparrows in the garden. One sparrow flew to the roof of the house, and I could not help wondering if the bird was a descendant of those brought to Philadelphia by Sparrow Jack.

Sparrow Jack's house is not a shrine—at least, not for most bird lovers. Many people visit Audubon's house on the Perkiomen Creek some twenty-odd miles away, but most of them have probably never heard of Sparrow House. It is not publicized. Rarely is it even mentioned as the place where John Bardsley conceived and carried out his sparrow project. In

fact, when the house was sold in 1908, the new own-
ers preferred to stress the Revolutionary War value
of the house. The sparrows were played down. And
so it is today. Local historical societies mention
Bardsley's house as an observation point during the
Battle of Germantown, but there is little in the ar-
chives about Sparrow Jack and his inchworm hunters.

Nor do many people know much about Sparrow
Jack himself. Audubon is famous, but Bardsley is
not. Audubon painted America's birds for posterity,
while John Bardsley, according to some, burdened
posterity with unwanted birds.

But I for one have always been grateful for the
abundance and tameness of the house sparrows.
Their presence and chirping, however monotonous,
have cheered me on many occasions. There have
been times when only the sparrows reminded me
that spring was not far away.

Years ago, when I attended elementary school in
Philadelphia, house sparrows were the only birds
that came into the schoolyard. This was not surpris-

ing; a concrete yard ringed with an iron fence does not attract wood thrushes, orioles, or other birds. Yet the dauntless sparrows hopped about the schoolyard, blending their chirps with the shouts of children.

I recall bleak November days in this schoolyard. Sparrows and children huddled on the leeward side of the stone building, away from the biting winds. Another boy, Abraham D'Ettis, and I often fed the birds. We pulled the crusts off our sandwich bread (we didn't like them anyway), broke them into small pieces, and tossed them to the hungry sparrows. The birds seemed thankful, for at recess and lunchtime on school days, they flocked into the schoolyard. Where they went and what they ate on weekends, I never knew.

I think the greatest value of the sparrows is their abundance. They are all around us. The city-bound boy or girl need not despair of learning about birds —not if he or she will be satisfied with a sparrow. The bird has interesting habits and its tameness permits a close view. To the boy or girl who would learn about birds, then, I say: look to the house sparrows

—they are an excellent way to learn the ABC's of bird watching or ornithology.

The house sparrows can be a source of various science class projects. For example, you might find out which insects the house sparrows catch in the spring and summer in your area or city. All you have to do is locate a sparrow nest, observe it without disturbing or frightening the birds, and determine the kinds of insects brought to the nestlings. If you want a more difficult project, try counting the number of insects carried by the male or female to the nest in one hour or a day!

Other projects involving sparrows come to mind. How many house sparrow nests can you find in your neighborhood? How many in one square mile? What do house sparrows use to build their nests in your city? When do sparrows nest in your region? How do the males defend their territories—by chirping, fighting, or what? How large is the sparrow territory? Does the female help defend it? At what time of day do the male and female work at nest-building? List all of the steps in the building of a sparrow's nest—

from gathering materials to the final structure. How soon after the nest is finished are the eggs laid? How many eggs? Which birds in your area get along with house sparrows? And which birds fight with them?

Perhaps you are interested in bird photography. If so, the house sparrows make good subjects. It is difficult to photograph wild birds in the field, but the house sparrows are fairly tame and can be photographed rather easily. After practicing with the sparrows, you can then try your hand with other birds.

Use a good camera. It is best to steady the camera by placing it on a tripod or other stand. Locate it to the south of the sparrow, if possible, as this location will put the bird in a better light. Otherwise, poor light will only give you a silhouette of the sparrow, a dark outline of the bird. There are a number of excellent books on outdoor photography; also booklets. They will give you some good tips on taking your sparrow photographs.

If you have a talent for sketching, try drawing a house sparrow. You can get close enough, if you are careful, without disturbing the birds. Sprinkle some birdseed around and your "models" will stay longer. If you decide to draw sparrows in color, make sure you have the proper light. Place your easel and yourself in a position which allows the sun's rays to fall on the bird, not behind it.

Many naturalists and ornithologists record bird calls and songs. Some bird songs are difficult to obtain; special equipment and patience are required. But you can record the different calls of house sparrows with an ordinary tape recorder. Locate a sparrow nest and—without disturbing the birds—set up your recorder. If the nest contains baby sparrows, so much the better. You can tape their peeping. When you do record sparrow calls, try to associate them with specific actions of the birds. For example, what notes do the males use when chasing another bird from the nest site or territory?

I'm sure that you can think of other sparrow projects. Perhaps you might turn up some valuable information about the birds and their habits. Granted they have been studied before, but there are many things about them we still do not know. And in the

past a number of amateur naturalists have made major contributions to ornithology.

If you are handy with tools and like to build things, try a sparrow house. House sparrows are easy to please when it comes to a home. Any box house with an opening of one-and-a-half inches will be suitable. Place the hole above the center of the box. Sparrows, like other birds, prefer to be hidden when incubating eggs. You may well be doing the other birds a favor too, by providing local house sparrows with boxes; at least, it may deter them from taking over the nests of other species.

House sparrows still bear the label of a public nuisance in many regions. In the suburban town where I live, for instance, they are unwelcome. Nobody in the town cares how much grain the house sparrows eat in the fields. Their chief complaint is that the sparrows eat most of the food in bird feeder stations. Bird food, particularly the packaged kind sold in supermarkets, is expensive and most people would rather feed chickadees, juncos, snow buntings, and other winter birds.

I have adopted the old saying, "If you can't lick them, join them," in my bird feeding practices. House sparrows eat a variety of foods which other birds will not. Therefore, I cater to the sparrows.

Into the bird feeders and onto the ground go large quantities of cheaper food: stale bread, crackers, cornflakes, and other food scraps. These extra rations do not prevent the sparrows from eating the fancier food in the feeder, but they do slow down consumption of the high-priced bird food mixtures.

So far, I have not won any converts to this practice. One person to whom I suggested the idea scoffed at me. He said I was only encouraging the house sparrows.

Occasionally I get drawn into discussions and arguments because of my fondness for the house sparrows. Recently I was accosted on the street by an acquaintance who is a staunch sparrow-hater. He does not harm them; he just hates them. When I asked him why, he gave the usual reasons, all of which I have written about in this book. "Sparrows are foreigners," he added. "They would never have been around here if it weren't for Sparrow Jack."

His statement caused me to think. Was what he said necessarily true? Would the house sparrow always have remained a strictly European species?

I wondered.

Japanese beetles and Norway rats came over here without an invitation or direct assistance. Why not the house sparrows? Yes, I decided, it was possible the sparrows could have found their way to North America accidentally or on their own initiative.

I knew, of course, that house sparrows were not migratory birds, at least not like swallows. If they migrated, it was only for relatively short, hardly noticeable distances. Some bird species "island hop" across large expanses of ocean, but this requires long and sustained flying, which the house sparrow cannot do. However, birds have been known to "hitch" rides on boats. In fact, three house sparrows hitched a ride on the U.S.S. *Blackhawk* in 1934 and traveled with the ship from the United States to China. The sparrows alternated between flying along after the ship and roosting on its stacks, wires, and other rigging when they were tired. These particular sparrows were outward bound, but doubtless some others entered the country in this fashion.

A recent bird immigrant—the cattle egret, a native of Africa and Asia—came to this hemisphere by boat. The bird is believed to have voyaged to North America by way of Guiana in South America.

Cattle egrets are not so numerous in this country as house sparrows. However, both their numbers and range are on the increase. These heron-like birds (called cattle egrets because they usually follow cattle, catching insects stirred up by the grazing animals) are now found from Florida to southern Canada and as far west as California. If these birds managed to gain a foothold in America—after arriving as stow-aways—house sparrows certainly could have done the same.

It was an interesting speculation, but I decided it would do no good to mention it to my sparrow-hating acquaintance. Besides, he had a look which suggested that he had thought up another sparrow-poser for me. And he had.

"Why," he demanded, "do you think the house sparrows survived and spread so rapidly after Sparrow Jack brought them to Philadelphia?"

I mentioned the reasons I thought were major factors in the survival and adaptation of the sparrows.

"Hah!" he exclaimed triumphantly. "You missed the most important reason of all."

"What is that?"

"House sparrows didn't have any enemies over here—they left them all behind in England."

"Not so," I replied. "What were the sparrow's enemies in England?"

He hesitated.

"I'll tell you," I said. Then I listed hawks, cats, weasels, and man. I quickly pointed out that all of these predators were in and around Philadelphia when the sparrows were imported in 1869.

Our conversation ended abruptly, for my acquaintance had to dash off to catch the 8:15 train to Philadelphia.

Popular birds or not, the house sparrows are here to stay. Naturally, they displaced native bird species in the past. There is bound to be disturbance whenever an alien species is introduced into an ecosystem, or wildlife community. That is why, for example, the United States Wildlife Service will not import wildlife from other countries for release into our wilderness areas.

However, I do not regard house sparrows as major threats to other birds today. Their population now is subject to natural checks and balances in many regions. We might say they have been absorbed into our wildlife communities.

Wherever they may live, the house sparrows are "naturalized" American birds; noisy, dirty, but always interesting. Go out and watch them. Listen to their chatter. In the words of Frank Dempster Sherman:

> *"Hark to the noisy caravan of brown*
> *Intrepid sparrows—Arabs of the air!"*

Suggested Reading

Unfortunately, there are no modern books about house sparrows. These birds are mentioned—or their appearance and habits described—in sections of some bird books and encyclopedias, including:

McGraw-Hill, *The Larousse Encyclopedia of Animal Life,* pages 462–63. New York, 1967.

National Geographic Society, *Song and Garden Birds of North America.* Washington, D.C., 1964.

Peterson, Roger Tory, *A Field Guide to the Birds.* Houghton Mifflin, Boston, 1947.

Zim, Herbert S., and Gabrielson, Ira N., *Birds* (Golden Nature Guide). Simon and Schuster, New York, 1949.

Glossary

Affinity: kinship or attractive relationship.

Agriculturist: a person trained in one or more of the many fields of agriculture, such as fruit culture, soil technology, crop production, etc.

Aphid: a plant louse, such as the rose aphid.

Chrysalis (plural, chrysalises): the pupa of some insects; the intermediate form that comes after the larval stage.

Covert, middle: a special feather that covers the base of the middle wing feathers.

Covert, tail: a feather that covers the base of a tail feather.

Cutworm: a caterpillar (actually a larva) that emerges at night to cut off the stems of young cabbage, bean, corn, and other plants.

Ecology: relationships between animals and their environment.

Ecosystem: a wildlife community and its living inhabitants.

Granary: storage place for grain.

Habitat: the natural place where a bird, mammal, reptile, etc., lives; for example, the city, woods, marsh, desert, etc.

Hieroglyphic: figure or character writing.

Horticulturist: a person who grows fruit, vegetables, flowers, ornamental plants, etc.

Imago: an insect in its final adult stage, usually sexually mature and winged.

Larva (plural larvae): the immature, wingless, and commonly wormlike stage of certain insects after they hatch from eggs—and in which they remain until ready to assume the pupa or chrysalis form.

Lore: the space between the eye and bill in birds.

Naturalist: a person who studies wildlife in its natural setting.

Oölogist: an ornithologist who specializes in the study of bird eggs.

Ornithologist: a zoologist who specializes in the study of birds.

Palearctic: primitive and northern.

Predator: a bird, mammal, reptile, etc., that lives off other animal forms.

Predatory: having the nature of a predator.

Weevil: any of a number of small beetles with snoutlike heads, such as the nut and boll weevils. The larvae of weevils eat out the center of nuts, fruit, and grain, or bore into trees and other plants.

Zoologist: a scientist who studies animal life and the classification of animals.

Index